Looking at
Animals
in
TREES

First published in Great Britain in 1999 by

 **Belitha Press Limited,**
London House, Great Eastern Wharf,
Parkgate Road, London SW11 4NQ

This edition first published in 2000

Series Editor Honor Head
Series Designer Hayley Cove
Picture Researcher Juliet Duff
Map Artwork Robin Carter / Wildlife Art Agency
Animal Symbols Arlene Adams

ISBN 1 84138 160 8 (paperback)
ISBN 1 84138 147 0 (big book)
ISBN 1 84138 023 7 (hardback)

Printed in China

10 9 8 7 6 5 4 3 2 1

British Library Cataloguing in Publication Data
for this book is available from the British Library

Photographic credits
Frank Lane Picture Agency: 7 S Maslowski, 8 L Lee Rue, 9 R Austing,
10 Martin Witners, 11 David Hosking, 12 Roger Wilmhurst, 13 Hugh Clark,
28 M Harvey 29 Brake/Sunset. NHPA: 18 Kevin Schafer,
20 James Carmichael Jnr, 22 Martin Wendler, 27 Stephen Dalton.
Oxford Scientific Films: 6 Zig Leszczynski. Planet Earth Pictures:
14 Richard Matthews, 15, 25 Ken Lucas, 16 Claus Meyer, 17 Peter J Oxford,
19 Tom Brakefield, 21 Brian Kenney, 23 J A Provenza, 24 Ken King,
26 Carol Farneti-Foster
Cover
NHPA: top left James Carmichael Jnr.
Planet Earth Pictures: top right Ken Lucas, bottom Richard Matthews.

Looking at
Animals
in
TREES

Moira Butterfield

Belitha Press

Introduction

Lots of trees together are called
forests or woods. Many forests
are in cold parts of the world,
where it snows nearly all year long.

Some forests are hot and steamy.
These are called rainforests. Here it
rains a lot but it is never cold or snowy.

Lots of different kinds of animals,
birds and insects live in the trees
in forests and woods. They all have
their own special way of finding
food and shelter in trees.

Contents

Squirrel

Squirrels live in nests in trees. The nests are called dreys. Squirrels have bushy tails which they use to help them balance when they climb trees.

Squirrels like to eat nuts, seeds, fruit and cones, so woods are a good place for them to find food.

Screech owl

At night-time screech owls fly down from their homes in the tree tops to hunt for food. They have large eyes, good hearing and sharp talons to catch voles and mice. When they have eaten fur and bones they cough them up in little balls called pellets.

Koala

Koalas live in the branches of eucalyptus trees in Australia. They never drink because they get all the juice they need from the tree leaves they munch.

Newborn koalas are only two centimetres long. They live in their mother's pouch until they are big enough to travel on her back.

Woodpecker

Woodpeckers have strong beaks to peck
holes in trees for their nests. They use
their long, sticky tongues to scoop out
bugs from under the tree bark.
When a woodpecker hammers hard
with its beak on a tree trunk it makes
a noise like a workman's drill.

Marmoset

Marmosets are small monkeys that live
in jungles. They have very long tails
which they wrap around branches to
help them swing through the trees.

Marmosets like to eat fruit and spiders.
They use their sharp teeth to gnaw holes
in trees so sap drips out for them to drink.

Fruit bat

These big bats are found in warm countries. They live in colonies close to trees where they can find fruit to eat. They have large eyes to see in the dark and a long nose to smell ripe fruit. They grab the fruit and crush it with their teeth to squeeze out the juice.

Macaw

These large parrots live in the rainforest.
They are easy to spot because they are
brightly coloured and noisy. They
can hold things with their claws.

Macaws use their sharp, hooked beaks
to split open tasty nuts and fruit that
grow in the forest around them.

Tree boa

A tree boa is a long, thin green snake that lives in rainforest trees. Even its eyes are green. It winds itself round a branch among the leaves so that nothing can see it. When it is hungry it swings out to catch passing birds to eat. It crushes them and swallows them whole.

Ocelot

Ocelots are wild jungle cats. Their stripy, spotty coats are good camouflage among the trees. They are expert climbers, so they easily catch birds and snakes to eat.

Baby ocelots are called kittens. They are born tiny and blind. Their mother looks after them until they grow stronger.

Bush baby

These furry little jungle creatures are nocturnal, which means they sleep all day and climb around the trees at night. They use their big eyes to see in the dark. To help find their way around in the gloom they spray scent on to trees to mark out their favourite pathways.

Tree frog

There are lots of different tree frogs. They have sticky discs on their toes to help them climb trees and strong back legs so they can leap up high to catch insects.

Rainforest tree frogs are brightly coloured with big eyes. During the day they sleep attached to the underside of a big leaf.

Sloth

Sloths spend nearly all their lives hanging upside down in the jungle trees of South America. They have long claws on each paw for gripping and climbing along branches. They move very slowly around their leafy home looking for plants to munch.

Where they live

This is a map of the world. It shows you where the animals live.

 Squirrel

 Screech owl

 Koala

 Woodpecker

 Marmoset

 Fruit bat

 Macaw

 Tree boa

 Ocelot

 Bush baby

 Tree frog

 Sloth

NORTH AMERICA

SOUTH AMERICA

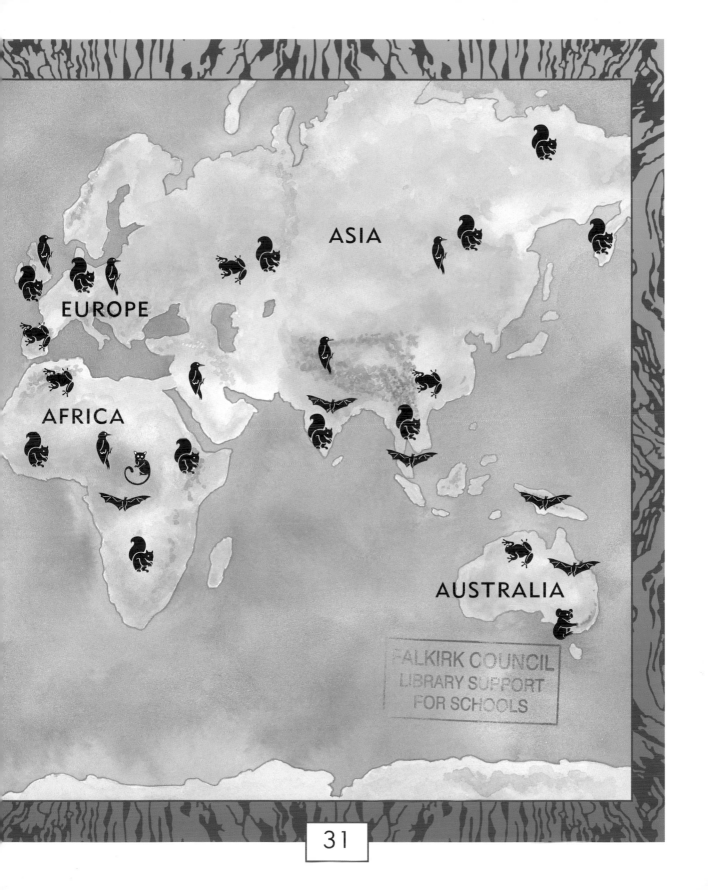

ASIA

EUROPE

AFRICA

AUSTRALIA

Index of words to learn